Steck-Vaughn

WORLD MYTHS

The Theft of Fire

Reviewer
Abdullahi A. Ibrahim
Fellow, Institute for the Advanced Study and Research
of the African Humanities, Northwestern University

STECK-VAUGHN
COMPANY
A Subsidiary of National Education Corporation

ISBN 0-8114-3371-4
Copyright © 1994 Steck-Vaughn Company.

2 3 4 5 6 7 8 9 0 SEC 99 98 97

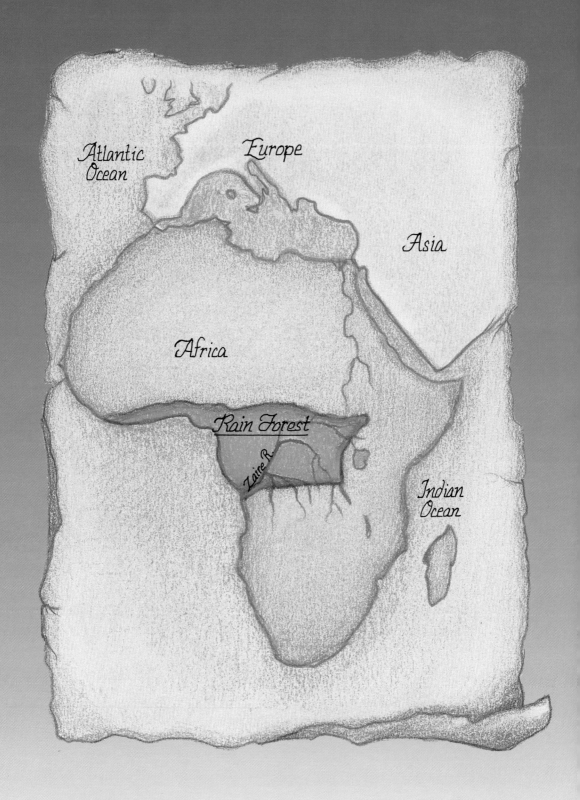

Atlantic
Ocean

Europe

Asia

Africa

Rain Forest

Zaire R.

Indian
Ocean

Introduction

Deep in the great rain forest of Central Africa live the Bambuti (bam BOO tee) people, whose adult members average under five feet in height. You can find their homeland on the map on page 2.

The Bambuti are probably the first inhabitants of the area, and their way of life has changed little in thousands of years. Many of them still live by hunting and gathering. The forest provides them with things they need to survive—meat, edible plants, fresh water, firewood, clothing, and shelter. The Bambuti have close relationships with neighboring groups that practice agriculture. Sometimes the Bambuti trade forest products, such as meat, honey, nuts, and mushrooms, to these neighbors for pots, axe blades, and crops.

Like many other people, the Bambuti considered fire so important that they explained its discovery in myths. They believed that they were the first humans to have fire, which they later shared with their crop-growing neighbors. In some stories, these forest people steal fire from their god. In the myth retold here, the Bambuti get fire from a much more surprising source! Besides the use of fire, what else does the story attempt to explain? What does the story tell you about the Bambuti's opinion of animals?

The Theft of Fire

Long ago, chimpanzees lived in the forest very much as humans do today. They spoke the same language as humans, lived in villages, and even knew how to grow and harvest bananas. And, of all the creatures, only chimpanzees possessed the secret of fire.

It seems that one day a young Bambuti hunter, armed with a net for catching game, left his camp to seek meat for his family. Game was scarce that day, and so the young man ventured deeper and deeper into the forest. Finally he spotted an antelope and eagerly followed it. The young hunter was so concerned with stalking his prey that he lost track of how far he had gone. Only when the antelope suddenly darted off did he notice that he was in a part of the forest completely unknown to him. There was no path to lead him back to his camp, and he could no longer see the sun. He tried to retrace his steps, but he became more and more unsure of his way as he walked.

At last, as night was falling, he stumbled to the edge of a clearing. It was filled with huts made from broad leaves that were

spread over wooden frames. It looked very much like a camp his own people might have set up. But instead of humans, he saw only chimpanzees.

The young hunter had heard his people speak of chimpanzee villages, but he had never seen one before. So he took cover behind a tree and watched with curiosity as the creatures greeted one another. He was most surprised to hear them converse in words that he could understand. As he listened, he learned that the older chimpanzees had just returned from their day's work. The younger chimps welcomed their elders with hugs, kisses, and words of joy.

In fact, the creatures were so pleasant and friendly that the hunter decided he had nothing to fear from them. So he stepped from behind the tree and spoke.

"My friends," he said bravely, "I am one of the Bambuti people. I lost my way as I was hunting an antelope. May I stay the night with you? Perhaps in the morning you will be able to show me the way back to my camp in the forest."

The chimpanzees were startled to meet a Bambuti hunter in this part of the forest. Some of the older ones knew tales about the Bambuti people, but only a few had ever seen one so close. Nevertheless, the leader of the chimpanzees greeted the young hunter politely.

"Welcome to our village, friend hunter," he smiled. "Of course, you are more than welcome to stay with us for the night. And when morning comes again, we will help you find your way home."

With that, the younger chimpanzees gathered around the hunter, gently poking and peering at him in friendly curiosity. They were especially interested in the bark cloth that he wore around his waist and in the hunting net he carried. Chattering happily, the youngsters led him past their huts toward the center of their village.

As they approached, the hunter saw a red glow coming from the open space in the midst of the huts. He felt the evening air growing warmer. Suddenly he stopped and gasped in fright. Before his eyes he saw flickering points of gold and crimson light leaping from a circle of glowing logs. The light seemed to change its form from moment to moment. What's more, the colors shifted and melted into one another endlessly. As the young hunter took in this wonderful sight, he found he had to turn away. His eyes hurt as they did when he tried to look at the sun.

"Has a piece of the sun fallen into the middle of your camp?" he asked his new friends in amazement.

At this, the young chimpanzees began to clap their hands in glee and jump up and down.

"Oh, no," laughed a young chimp who had taken a particular interest in the hunter. "This is the thing we call fire. It does seem like the sun, but it is not part of it at all. Fire is both wonderful and terrible. But if you tend it carefully, it will not harm you. As long as you feed it with dry logs, it will keep flickering and glowing."

"But what does this fire thing do?" the hunter asked his host.

"We consider it a great friend," answered the young chimpanzee, pulling the young man closer to the flaming logs. "You see, when the air turns cool, we just sit near the fire and it warms our bodies."

The hunter stretched his hands toward the fire and felt a comforting warmth move up his arms.

"This feels wonderful," he said to his new friend. The two joined the other chimpanzees as they sat around the fire. "The light of this fire helps you see things in the dark, too."

"Yes," replied the chimpanzee. "And the other animals are terrified of fire, so it keeps them away from us while we sleep. But we always must watch the fire and control its burning. Otherwise it could turn against us and destroy us. It could feed on our huts and on the trees of the forest."

Suddenly, two chimpanzees appeared carrying sharpened sticks over their shoulders. Pieces of raw meat were strung on each stick. The chimpanzees propped up the sticks with stones so that the pieces of meat were held over the fire.

The hunter watched with great interest as the meat began to sputter and turn color. Every few minutes a chimp would turn the sticks so that the heat from the fire reached another part of the meat. Along with the sight and sound, the young man was amazed at the smell that reached his nostrils. He had not noticed before how hungry he was, but now his mouth began to water.

"What is this?" he said. "What is this fire thing doing to your meat?"

Again the chimps showed their delight at the visitor's questions by jumping up and down and clapping their hands. "Cooking! Cooking!" they all chattered. "We are cooking our meat!"

"You see," explained the young chimp who had taken it upon himself to teach the visitor, "the fire changes the meat so that it becomes softer and easier to chew. And it tastes better after the fire has cooked it."

When they gave some of the cooked meat to the young hunter, he had to agree. In fact, he thought he had never eaten anything so delicious.

As he licked the warm juices from his fingers, an idea began to form in his mind. This fire was a true marvel! Surely his people would find it as useful as the chimpanzees did. Its warmth and light would make their nights much safer. And once they tasted what it could do to meat . . . !

After a good night's sleep, the hunter, with the help of a chimpanzee guide, found his way back to his camp. He kept quiet about the miraculous thing he had witnessed in the village, but he couldn't stop thinking about it.

A few days later, the young hunter decided to pay his new friends another visit. He wanted to learn more about fire. When he arrived at the village at midday, he found only the young chimps there, feeding logs to the fire and tending to other chores. The older chimps were all off at their plantation, taking care of the banana crop.

"Welcome back!" called the hunter's special friend, who was delighted to see him again. "Come, sit here by the fire and have some bananas!"

For the rest of the afternoon, the chimpanzees entertained their new friend with songs and stories. Trying to show as little interest in the fire as possible, the young man still watched it closely. He carefully noted just how to feed it and how to keep it from spreading. He learned how far from the fire to set the cooking sticks and how often to turn them.

When the hunter went home in the late afternoon, he felt sure that he knew enough to tend a fire and roast meat in his own camp. There was only one problem—how could he start a fire in the first place? That was something the young hunter had not seen his chimpanzee friends do. He hesitated to ask, for fear that it was a secret they might be unwilling to share. He decided his best hope of bringing fire to his people was to steal it.

So a few days later, with a plan well in mind, he traveled again to the village of the chimpanzees. Once again, he arrived in the middle of the day, when the older chimps were away. This time, the young hunter wore a new bark cloth around his waist, which hung all the way to the ground. As before, the young chimpanzees welcomed him with cheerful chattering and clapping. They found his new bark cloth an object of wonder and the source of friendly jokes.

"Sit down quickly," said one chimp, "before you trip over your bark cloth and hurt yourself!"

"Why, that bark cloth is so long you could wrap yourself up in it three times!" cried another, laughing.

As he had done on his earlier visits, the young man warmed himself by the fire and munched the sweet bananas his hosts offered him. As the afternoon wore on, he inched his way closer and closer to the fire. Finally, he was so close that the edge of his bark cloth began to smoke.

"Be careful, my friend," cried a young chimp in alarm, "or our fire will eat up your fancy new bark cloth."

"Don't worry," joked the hunter. "This cloth is plenty long. I won't mind if it's a little shorter." With that he moved even closer to the fire. Suddenly, a small flame leaped from the corner of the bark cloth. The hunter didn't waste a second. He jumped to his feet and rushed out of the village. The chimpanzees were so astounded at this that they stood, gaping. As they watched, the young hunter disappeared with his burning bark cloth into the deep forest.

"Now why did our Bambuti friend do that?" said one, scratching his head in puzzlement.

"We could have easily put out the fire," added another, as she pursed her lips and frowned. "Maybe he doesn't know the fire can hurt him."

"Perhaps we should try to find him," suggested a third, "to make sure he hasn't burned himself."

The young chimps were so upset by what had happened that they called their elders home from the plantation. After much chattering discussion, a party of elders was at last sent to track the Bambuti hunter through the forest. But long before the creatures had decided what to do, their friend had reached his camp. And by the time the chimps found him safe at home, he had used his burning bark cloth to light fires for his people. The fires glowed everywhere as the troop of chimpanzees entered the Bambuti camp, and the hunter was already teaching his people how to cook meat.

The chimpanzees were astounded. They began to jump about and shriek in anger. "You have stolen our fire," cried the oldest, as he looked around the camp in dismay. "We treated you well when you lost your way, and you have repaid us with robbery!"

"If you had asked us," said another ancient one, "we would have willingly told you the secret of our fire!"

"Yes, you should have done the honest thing and asked us," added a third.

Seeing that they were outnumbered, the chimpanzees decided it would be foolish to turn their anger and disappointment into a fight. So, grumbling at their betrayal, they returned sadly to their village. They vowed never again to befriend any human being.

The chimpanzees were so distressed by the way their Bambuti friend had treated them that they left their village and moved into the forest. Since then, chimpanzees have gone without bananas, eating only wild fruit. And, of course, they have long forgotten the secret of fire.

Glossary

agriculture *n*. Farming; the raising of crops for food and other uses. p. 3

astounded *adj*. Amazed; surprised and shocked. p. 13

befriend *v*. To make friends with. p. 15

betrayal *n*. An act of cheating or giving away someone else's secrets. p. 15

converse *v*. To talk with someone. p. 5

edible *adj*. Able to be eaten. p. 3

outnumbered *adj*. Having forces much smaller in number than others. p. 15

purse *v*. To draw together or wrinkle up. p. 13

puzzlement *n*. Confusion; having trouble understanding. p. 13

repay *v*. To pay back. p. 13

Acknowledgments

Steck-Vaughn Company

Executive Editor Diane Sharpe
Senior Editor Martin S. Saiewitz
Assistant Art Director Cynthia Ellis

Proof Positive/Farrowlyne Associates, Inc.

Program Development, Design, Illustration, and Production